Spring Harve
Bible Workb

Wholehearted:
reflections on
worship, justice
and the faithfulness
of God

Malachi

Spring Harvest
Equipping the Church for action

First published in 2011 by Elevation for Spring Harvest

Elevation is part of Memralife Group, registered charity number 1126997, a company limited by guarantee, registered in England and Wales, number 6667924. 14 Horsted Square, Uckfield, East Sussex, TN22 1QG

The right of Ruth Valerio to be identified as the Author of this Word has been asserted by her in accordance with Copyright, Designs and Patents Act 1988

British Library Cataloguing in Publication Data

A catalogue record for this book is available from the British Library

ISBN 978-1-899788-78-1

Typeset by Ascent Creative
Cover design by Paul Lewis Design
Printed in Great Britain by Halcyon

Contents

About this book

This book is written primarily for use in a group situation, but can easily be used by individuals who want to study the book of Malachi. It can be used in a variety of contexts, so it is perhaps helpful to spell out the assumptions that we have made about the groups that will use it. These can have a variety of names – homegroups, Bible study groups, cell groups – we've used group as the generic term.

- The emphasis of the studies will be on the application of the Bible. Group members will not just learn facts, but will be encouraged to think 'How does this apply to me? What change does it require of me? What incidents or situations in my life is this relevant to?'

- Groups can encourage honesty and make space for questions and doubts. The aim of the studies is not to find the 'right answer', but to help members understand the Bible by working through their questions. The Christian faith throws up paradoxes. Events in people's lives may make particular verses difficult to understand. The group should be a safe place to express these concerns.

- Groups can give opportunities for deep friendships to develop. Group members will be encouraged to talk about their experiences, feelings, questions, hopes and fears. They will be able to offer one another pastoral support and to get involved in each other's lives.

- There is a difference between being a collection of individuals who happen to meet together every Wednesday and being an effective group who bounce ideas off each other, spark inspiration and creativity, pooling their talents and resources to create solutions together: one whose whole is definitely greater than the sum of its parts. The process of working through these studies will encourage healthy group dynamics.

Space is given for you to write answers, comments, questions and thoughts. This book will not tell you what to think, but will help you discover the truth of God's word through thinking, discussing, praying and listening.

FOR GROUP MEMBERS

- You will probably get more out of the study if you spend some time during the week reading the passage and thinking about the questions. Make a note of anything you don't understand.

- Pray that God will help you to understand the passage and show you how to apply it. Pray for other members in the group too, that they will find the study helpful.

- Be willing to take part in the discussions. The leader of the group is not there as an expert with all the answers. They will want everyone to get involved and share their thoughts and opinions.

- However, don't dominate the group! If you are aware that you are saying a lot, make space for others to contribute. Be sensitive to other group members and aim to be encouraging. If you disagree with someone, say so but without putting down their contribution.

FOR INDIVIDUALS

- Although this book is written with a group in mind, it can also be easily used by individuals. You obviously won't be able to do the group activities suggested, but you can consider how you would answer the questions and write your thoughts in the space provided.

- You may find it helpful to talk to a prayer partner about what you have learnt, and ask them to pray for you as you try and apply what you are learning to your life.

- The New International Version of the text is printed in the book. If you use a different version, then read from your own Bible as well.

Introduction to MALACHI

'How can this happen to me if God loves me?'

'Where is the God of justice?'

'What's the point in serving God? It doesn't seem to make my life any better'.

'I'll just give God the minimum and keep the rest for myself'.

'I'll keep up the pretence of worship then no one will know what's really going on underneath'.

Have you ever heard anyone say the above or live in a way that reflects those statements and questions? Maybe there have been times when that person has been you! The Israelites were saying things along very similar lines and Malachi tackles the issues they raise head on.

The prophecy was spoken during the period of Israel's return from exile, probably after Ezra arrived back in Judah in 458BC and during the time of Nehemiah, who returned in 444BC. It is probably just short of a hundred years since the first Israelites came back from Babylon; worship in the temple would have been well established and the people would have been trying to get on with their lives and settle back into being a nation after the traumas of the exile.

Malachi is therefore talking into a situation, not of crisis, but of everyday life, albeit an everyday life that is a struggle. And the picture we see here is not a flattering one. We see a group of people who are far from being wholehearted in their worship of God: not living lives of righteousness, but effectively doing as little as they think they can get away with. They keep up a pretence of worship whilst underneath they blame God for the situation they find themselves in and have little confidence that he can do anything to change things.

But, amidst the harsh words that God speaks to the people through Malachi, he has two overriding things that he wants to say: '**I have loved you**' (1:2) and

'I, the LORD, do not change' (3:6). He points them to look in three directions to see the proof of this. Firstly, he gets them to look beyond their borders at the Edomites to see what their fate could have been. Unlike the Edomites, they have been brought back from exile and restored to their own land (1:4-5). Secondly, he gets them to look at themselves, saying bluntly that their hard times are because of their own sins and that they could choose an alternative (eg. 3:8-12). And thirdly, he gets them to lift up their eyes and look to the future, to that day when his chosen one will come and sort out the righteous from the unrighteous and will demonstrate that God does care and will act (3:1-5, 4:1-6).

We may ourselves be in a time of peace and blessing and feel far removed from what Israel was struggling with in Malachi's day, or we may find that their questions and statements to God have some resonance in our own lives. Whatever situation we are currently in there is much to learn from Malachi's words, much to be challenged with, and much to be encouraged by, as we seek to live lives of wholehearted devotion to God.

Session 1: God's Unfailing Love

 AIM: To re-discover God's love for Israel and for us.

TO SET THE SCENE

Malachi is the last book of the Old Testament, but do you know how it fits into the story of God's dealings with his people, Israel? Do this exercise together to find out:

Take sheets of paper and write on them the major events of the Old Testament, one on each piece of paper (eg. Creation, Joseph, Exodus etc). Work together at trying to remember as many as you can, but don't worry about chronological order at this stage. Then put the sheets on the floor and together arrange them in a time line. Take some time to look at the story in front of you, making sure that, as a group, you all understand how the pieces fit together.

Read the passage together:

An oracle: The word of the LORD to Israel through Malachi.

Jacob Loved, Esau Hated

"I have loved you", says the LORD.

"But you ask, 'How have you loved us?'

"Was not Esau Jacob's brother?" the LORD says. "Yet I have loved Jacob, but Esau I have hated, and I have turned his mountains into a wasteland and left his inheritance to the desert jackals."

Edom may say, "Though we have been crushed, we will rebuild the ruins".

But this is what the LORD Almighty says:

"They will be called the Wicked Land, a people always under the wrath of the LORD. You will see it with your own eyes and say, 'Great is the LORD – even beyond the borders of Israel!'"

Malachi 1:1-5

With these first five verses, Malachi throws down the gauntlet to the people of Israel. 'I have loved you', he declares, there is no beating around the bush with God!

But Israel is not going to be convinced quite so easily. With a mixture of arrogance and sullenness, the people stare back at God and challenge him with the question, 'How have you loved us'? It is a question they may well feel they have a right to ask God as they find themselves in the midst of the mess of trying to re-build their nation after the ravages of the exile.

And it is a question that we might sometimes feel we want to throw back at God too, whether in our own lives or in our lives together as church. But whatever we want to challenge God with, his declaraton to us stands firm and his love stands firm.

DISCUSS TOGETHER

1. Were any of you able to read through the whole of Malachi before this first session, or have you read it all through before? What are your initial impressions? The word for 'oracle' in verse 1 literally means 'burden' and is a threatening way to start the prophecy. How do you feel about studying such a potentially ominous book of the Bible?

2. Throughout Malachi, Israel responds to God's words by throwing questions back at him. In what ways have you seen children using questions to avoid something they do not want to hear? Can you think of ways in which you use this technique yourself?

What does the Bible say? **3.** Despite the ominous start, the first thing we hear from God is the phrase, 'I have loved you'. Divide into twos or threes and take some time to look at some of the references in the Old Testament to God's love. Use your concordances to do a word search. What do you learn about God's love from the verses you have found? Come back and talk together about what you have found.

4. In this last book of the Old Testament, verses 2-3 refer right back to the very beginnings of Israel's life in the first book, Genesis. Remind yourselves of what happened by reading Genesis 25:19-34. How is God using the story of these

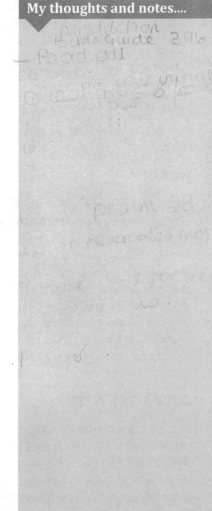

My thoughts and notes....

two brothers to demonstrate his unfailing love for Israel?

 5. As God uses Israel's history to assure her of his love, so he can use ours too. Where have you seen God's love at work in your life?

 6. And yet have there been times when you have doubted if God's statement, 'I have loved you', is really true? What happened? How did you work through that?

 7. In her commentary on Malachi, Joyce Baldwin describes the time when Malachi was speaking as a time of 'waiting'. How could our own time as a church be described as a time of waiting?

 8. Do you think the Church today ever has reason to ask God, 'how have you loved us?'? If so, what reply might God give?

WORSHIP

Psalm 23 is perhaps one of the finest descriptions of God's love for us. Use it now as a basis for your worship together. You might like to have someone read it out a couple of times over, quite slowly so as to give people time to take in all that is being said. You could suggest that people share which parts of the psalm most resonate with them, or you could simply sit in silence for a few minutes to give people time for their own reflections. Finish by praying together, thanking God for the way that he loves us.

DURING THE WEEK

Malachi 1:5 is a resounding conclusion to today's passage and shows the impact that God's love should have both on ourselves and on those with whom we meet day to day. Try to find ways to carry this verse with you throughout this week and use it as a basis for your prayers, that people might see God's love working in you in such a way that it leads them to acknowledge God's presence and to praise him. Don't be afraid to ask God to give you particular 'moments' with people.

FOR FURTHER STUDY

- Charles Swindoll, *The Grace Awakening* (Thomas Nelson, 2006)

- Kevin Vanhoozer (ed.), *Nothing Greater, Nothing Better: Theological Essays on the Love of God* (Eerdmans Publishing Co, 2001)

- Philip Yancey, *What's So Amazing About Grace?* (Zondervan, 2002)

- Joyce Baldwin, *Haggai, Zechariah, Malachi (Tyndale Old Testament Commentaries)* (InterVarsity Press, 2009)

Session 2: Giving Worship

 AIM: To consider what we bring God in our worship

TO SET THE SCENE

Every family has their own rituals and protocols for giving and receiving presents, whether for birthdays or other special occasions, or even just simply for love. Go round the group and talk about how you 'do' presents in your family.

Read the passage together:

"A son honours his father, and a servant his master. If I am a father, where is the honour due to me? If I am a master, where is the respect due to me?" says the LORD Almighty. "It is you, O priests, who show contempt for my name.

"But you ask, 'How have we shown contempt for your name?'

"You place defiled food on my altar.

But you ask, 'How have we defiled you?'

"By saying that the LORD's table is contemptible. When you bring blind animals for sacrifice, is that not wrong? When you sacrifice crippled or diseased animals, is that not wrong? Try offering them to your governor! Would he be pleased with you? Would he accept you?" says the LORD Almighty.

"Now implore God to be gracious to us. With such offerings from your hands, will he accept you?" – says the LORD Almighty.

"Oh, that one of you would shut the temple doors, so that you would not light useless fires on my altar! I am not pleased with you", says the LORD Almighty, "and I will accept no offering from your hands. My name will be great among the nations, from the rising to the setting of the sun. In every place incense and pure offerings will be brought to my name, because my name will be great among the nations", says the LORD Almighty.

"But you profane it by saying of the Lord's table, 'It is defiled', and of its food, 'It is contemptible'. And you say, 'What a burden!' and you sniff at it contemptuously," says the LORD Almighty.

"When you bring injured, crippled or diseased animals and offer them as sacrifices, should I accept them from your hands?" says the LORD. "Cursed is the cheat who has an acceptable male in his flock and vows to give it, but then sacrifices a blemished animal to the Lord. For I am a great king", says the LORD Almighty, "and my name is to be feared among the nations".

Malachi 1:6-14

This passage is addressed predominantly to the priests of Israel and reveals a terrible situation where the priests are bringing second-rate gifts to God as part of their worship. With verse 14, though, Yahweh's words are thrown open to include everyone, not just the priests, because of course where did the inferior gifts come from, if not from the people? The shallowness of the people's worship is contrasted with the richness of God's love that we saw in our first session and God accuses the people of showing contempt for his name, dishonouring him through the gifts that they are bringing.

There is a challenge for us here too. How can we ensure that our worship today is not shallow but is reflective of who God is and what he has done for us?

DISCUSS TOGETHER

1. In verse 6 the word for 'honour' is actually translated 'fear' in other parts of the Old Testament. The concept of 'the fear of the Lord' is a regular theme in the Old Testament and is an attitude that is encouraged. Divide people into pairs and send them off with a Bible concordance to do a brief study on fearing the Lord. Then come back together to talk about what you have learnt.

2. Malachi compares God's response to the inadequacies of Israel's gifts with the response that they would receive from the governor if they were to bring something similar. If he were speaking today, what analogy might he use?

3. Read the story of the widow's offering in Luke 21:3. How might you use this story to explain to the people of Malachi's time what they were doing wrong?

4. The Israelites clearly struggled with giving God the best, preferring instead to give him things that were

> **My thoughts and notes....**

not so precious and hence were easier to part with. Are there things that you find easier to give to God, and what things do you find harder?

 5. Do you think it is important to be in a church in which the corporate style of worship is one that you enjoy?

6. The people talked about their worship as being a 'burden' (verse 13), as if they felt that they had better things to be spending their time on. Do you sometimes feel a bit resentful at having to spend time worshipping God with other people? How do you deal with those feelings when they arise?

7. 'What can I give Him, poor as I am?
If I were a shepherd, I would bring a lamb;
If I were a Wise Man, I would do my part;
Yet what I can I give Him: give my heart.'

What do the words of this famous Christmas carol have to say into the passage that we are looking at today?

 8. The priests here seem to be encouraging 'cheap worship' that doesn't give God the best. Are there ways in which our churches today encourage 'cheap worship' too? How can we respond?

WORSHIP

Psalm 148 is a wonderful song of worship. Read it out loud together and then try writing your own psalm. Get a piece of paper and ask one person to make up the first line of a psalm and then write it at the head of the paper. Fold over that line and pass it to the next person, who then writes a second line, folds it over and passes it on. Continue until everyone has written a line, then open up the paper and read out your psalm. Use this as a basis for a time of worship and prayer together.

DURING THE WEEK

This week, make it a special focus of your prayers to pray for the people who lead worship in your church and for your church leaders. As you get closer to Sunday turn your thoughts to the forthcoming service or meeting and be praying for that, for whatever you feel is appropriate for your church.

FOR FURTHER STUDY

Corporate worship is such a central part of our lives as Christians: so much so that it is easy to do it without giving it a second thought, or just to leave it up to those who take on that responsibility. And yet we are all responsible for the worshipping lives of our churches. Why not take some time to do some deeper reading and thinking around this whole area: you might be surprised what you learn!

Some good books to read are:

- Harold Best, *Unceasing Worship* (InterVarsity Press, 2003)

- Andrew Burnham, *Heaven and Earth in Little Space* (Canterbury Press, 2010)

- Bob Kauflin, *Worship Matters* (Crossway, 2008)

- Robert Webber, *Ancient-Future Worship: Proclaiming and Enacting God's Narrative* (Baker Books, 2008)

Good Resources:

- www.engageworship.org

- www.womeninworshipnetwork.com

Session 3: Faithful Worship

 AIM: To consider the challenges that Malachi 2 brings to us as we seek to be faithful worshippers in all areas of our lives.

TO SET THE SCENE

Talk about your experiences of leadership. What good and bad experiences have you had? Who are the leaders in your current situations and what are they like? If you are the leader, how do you find it? What do you enjoy about it and what do you find difficult?

Read the passage together:

"And now this admonition is for you, O priests. If you do not listen, and if you do not set your heart to honour my name", says the LORD Almighty, "I will send a curse upon you, and I will curse your blessings. Yes, I have already cursed them, because you have not set your heart to honour me.

"Because of you I will rebuke your descendants; I will spread on your faces the offal from your festival sacrifices, and you will be carried off with it. And you will know that I have sent you this admonition so that my covenant with Levi may continue", says the LORD Almighty.

"My covenant was with him, a covenant of life and peace, and I gave them to him; this called for reverence and he revered me and stood in awe of my name. True instruction was in his mouth and nothing false was found on his lips. He walked with me in peace and uprightness, and turned many from sin.

"For the lips of a priest ought to preserve knowledge, and from his mouth men should seek instruction – because he is the messenger of the LORD Almighty. But you have turned from the way and by your teaching have caused many to stumble; you have violated the covenant with Levi", says the LORD Almighty. "So I have caused you to be despised and humiliated before all the people, because you have not followed my way but have shown partiality in matters of the law".

Have we not all one Father? Did not one God create us? Why do we profane the covenant of our fathers by breaking faith with one another?

Judah has broken faith. A detestable thing has been committed in Israel and in

Jerusalem: Judah has desecrated the sanctuary the LORD lives, by marrying the daughter of a foreign god. As for the man who does this, whoever he may be, may the LORD cut him off from the tents of Jacob – even though he brings offerings to the LORD Almighty.

Another thing you do: You flood the LORD's altar with tears. You weep and wail because he no longer pays attention to your offerings or accepts them with pleasure from your hands. You ask, "Why?" It is because the LORD is acting as the witness between you and the wife of your youth, because you have broken faith with her, though she is your partner, the wife of your marriage covenant.

Has not the LORD made them one? In flesh and spirit they are his. And why one? Because he was seeking godly offspring. So guard yourself in your spirit, and do not break faith with the wife of your youth.

"I hate divorce", says the LORD God of Israel, "and I hate a man's covering of himself with violence as well as with his garment", says the LORD Almighty.

So guard yourself in your spirit, and do not break faith.

Malachi 2:1-16

The pace does not let up as Malachi continues his assault on Israel's priests, carrying on with the theme of false worship that we saw in our last session. What we see happening in this chapter is the focus changing from what happens during the actual acts of worship to how the priests, and then the people in general (from verse 10), are behaving in general. God's complaint is not just that they worship him with inferior gifts, but that their whole lives bring dishonour to him.

So for us, too, we are worshipping God as much when we are keeping faithful in our marriages, working for unity in our church and displaying integrity in our workplace as when we are in church on a Sunday.

DISCUSS TOGETHER

My thoughts and notes....

1. The phrase 'my name' (verse 2) is used nine times in the book of Malachi. The New Bible Dictionary states that 'The name is a summary way of stating what God is in himself (his name is all that is known to be true about him and his motives of action) and also what God is to others, allowing them to know his name (letting them into his truth) and sharing his name with them (letting them into his fellowship)'.[1]

---

1   *New Bible Dictionary (IVP: 1992), 812*

Make a list of the words that the Bible uses to describe God. And then talk together about what words we would use to describe God today; what do we know about him to be true?

 2. The words about blessings and curses in verse 2 may well refer back to Deuteronomy 28, in which Moses lays out the stark choice facing the people of Israel as they stand at the threshold of the promised land: will they obey God and be blessed, or disobey God and be cursed? Look together at what those blessings and curses entail.

3. The blessings are turned into curses because the priests have not honoured the Lord's name. In what ways do you think that can happen today?

4. Do you know the background behind Malachi's words about Levi? If not, look together at Numbers 3 and 4, which describe the setting apart of the Levitical tribe to be assistants to the priests of Israel. (Use the Leaders' Notes to help everyone to understand).

 5. Levi is being used by Malachi to illustrate how the priesthood should function. Go through verses 5-7 and put the different points into your own words. What relevance do these descriptions have to your own church leaders? Are there particular points that you think are most important today?

6. Are there people in your group who are in positions of leadership? Ask them to talk about what relevance verses 5-7 has for them in their situations.

 7. Verse 10 sounds like it could have come from the New Testament! What verses or passages does it remind you of?

8. Malachi is looking at the particular issue of mixed marriages, which was causing problems in that context. What are some of our issues today that cause us to 'break faith with one another'?

How can we take steps to move forward positively?

9. Divorce was clearly a big issue in Malachi's day, as it is for us now. In what ways do you think Malachi's words in verses 13-16 are relevant today?

10. Do you know anyone currently going through divorce or experiencing its pain? If so, take some time now to pray for them.

WORSHIP

Go back to question 1 and to the descriptions and words about God that you came up with. Ask someone to read them out and then put the list on the floor in the middle of you all, or put it somewhere where everyone can see it. Use your list as the basis for you now to worship God, praising him for everything that is on your list.

DURING THE WEEK

Today's passage is addressed to the priests, and then from verse 10 the scope seems to broaden out to include all the people. How much thought do you give through the week to the person/people who lead your church? Maybe you are just aware of them on a Sunday and then forget about them for the rest of the week! This week, try to pray for them each day and find a way to keep them in your thoughts. Maybe you could contact them after this session or tomorrow and ask them if there is anything particular that they would like you to pray about, or anything practical that you could do for them.

In addition, if there were people in your group for whom question 6 was relevant, ask them what you can pray for this week and remember to do so.

FOR FURTHER STUDY

The whole area of divorce and remarriage is a huge one for our society today, with Christians by no means united on what our approach should be. Are your opinions well thought-through and informed? If you think you would benefit by doing some more thinking on the subject, then here are some helpful things to read:

- Andrew Cornes, *Divorce and Remarriage: Biblical principle and pastoral practice* (Hodder and Stoughton, 1993)

- Graeme Davidson, *When the Vow Breaks: Contemplating Christian Divorce* (SPCK, 2009)

- Wendy Foxall, *Surviving the Storm: Finding God in the midst of a marriage breakdown* (Sovereign Word, 2004)

- David Instone-Brewer, *Divorce and Remarriage in the Church: Biblical solutions for pastoral realities* (Paternoster Press, 2003)

Session 4: Just Worship

 AIM: To see how God remains unchanging and faithful whatever Israel does, and to consider the issues facing Israel and see how we can learn from them.

TO SET THE SCENE

Go on, be honest – what would you do if you won or inherited a large amount of money?!

Read the passage together:

You have wearied the LORD with your words.

"How have we wearied him?" you ask.

By saying, "All who do evil are good in the eyes of the LORD, and he is pleased with them" or "where is the God of justice?"

"See, I will send my messenger, who will prepare the way before me. Then suddenly the LORD you are seeking will come to his temple; the messenger of the covenant, whom you desire, will come," says the Lord Almighty.

But who can endure the day of his coming? Who can stand when he appears? For he will be like a refiner's fire or a launderer's soap. He will sit as a refiner and purifier of silver; he will purify the Levites and refine them like gold and silver. Then the LORD will have men who will bring offerings in righteousness, and the offerings of Judah and Jerusalem will be acceptable to the LORD, as in days gone by, as in former years.

"So I will come near to you for judgement, I will be quick to testify against sorcerers, adulterers and perjurers, against those who defraud labourers of their wages, who oppress the widows and the fatherless, and deprive aliens of justice, but do not fear me," says the LORD Almighty.

"I, the LORD do not change. So you, O descendants of Jacob, are not destroyed. Ever since the time of your forefathers you have turned away from my decrees and have not kept them. Return to me, and I will return to you," says the LORD Almighty.

"But you ask, 'How are we to return?'

"Will a man rob God? Yet you rob me.

"But you ask, 'How do we rob you?'

"In tithes and offerings. You are under a curse – the whole nation of you – because you are robbing me. Bring the whole tithe into the storehouse, that there may be food in my house. Test me in this," says the LORD Almighty, "and see if I will not throw open the floodgates of heaven and pour out so much blessing that you will not have room enough for it. I will prevent pests from devouring your crops, and the vines in your fields will not cast their fruit," says the LORD Almighty. "Then all the nations will call you blessed, for yours will be a delightful land," says the LORD Almighty.

Malachi 2:17-3:12

This passage hits us straight between the eyes with one of the biggest issues facing us as God-believers: where is the God of justice when we are faced with a world that is so full of evil and injustice? The Israelites were throwing this question at God and using it as an excuse not to take him, or their worship of him, seriously. But God does not let them off the hook and he turns it back onto them. A day is coming, he says, when they will see once and for all that he is not inactive and then their actions will be revealed for what they really are.

In contrast to the God who does not change, Israel is called to change and return to him. The two big issues for them revolve around justice and generosity; and these issues are relevant for us today as they ever were then.

DISCUSS TOGETHER

My thoughts and notes....

1. Look at what the Israelites say to God in 2:17. Put what they are saying into your own words. What situation do you think they were in as a nation that led to them saying these things?

 How does this apply to me? In what ways can you relate to what is being said here? How have you worked this out in your own thinking?

2. How does 3:1 answer the Israelites' question in 2:17?

3. Malachi 3:1-4 would seem to have three persons in view: (1) the Lord Almighty, (2) the preparing messenger, and (3) the Lord, or messenger of the covenant. Do you think we can see persons (2) and (3) as referring to John the

Baptist and Jesus? If so, what can we learn from this about why God the Father sent Jesus to us?

4. 3:5 mentions seven particular sins. What are they and where do we see those sins today?

 5. Dom Helder Camara, a former Brazilian bishop, said, 'When I give food to the poor they call me a saint. When I ask why the poor have no food, they call me a communist'. What do you think about that quote? Is there anything you can do to respond to poverty yourself?

6. Talking about 3:6, Walter Kaiser says, 'God can change in his actions toward us as much as any other living person can change. What he cannot and will not change, however, is the consistency of his own person as the basis on which these decisions are made. That is the comforting feature of his unchangeableness'.[2]

What do you think about God's unchangeableness?

 Have there been particular moments in your life when that has been of comfort to you? Or maybe particular moments when it has caused you discomfort?

7. Israel are under God's judgement because they are skimping on how much they give to him and are not giving him their full tithe. Do you think the concept of tithing still applies to Christians today?

8. Verses 8-12 should encourage us to be generous with our money. Are there particular people you know who give you a good example of generosity?

 9. A Joseph Rowntree survey found that 95% of those questioned

---

2 *Walter C Kaiser Jr, God's Unchanging Love (Baker Books, 1984), 77.*

found it offensive to be asked about how they spent their money and whether the choices they were making could be improved upon. Would you put yourself in that 95%?

WORSHIP

We worship and serve an incredibly generous God. Go round the group and ask people to say what they feel particularly thankful for, that God has given them in their own life. Spend time together thanking God for the way he has blessed us in so many ways.

DURING THE WEEK

There is a challenge in today's passage to be generous with our money. Is this an area in which you want to be developed? If so, ask God to give you opportunities to put this into practice this week, and be on the look out for those openings. Be warned – God might just listen to your prayer and take you seriously!

FOR FURTHER STUDY

The Bible has so much to say about the subject of money, and we spend so much of our lives earning it and spending it, and yet it is not something that we tend to take the time to look at. If you would like to change that, then here are some good books to read.

- Craig Blomberg, *Neither Poverty Nor Riches: A biblical theology of possessions* (Apollos InterVarsity Press, 1999)

- Mark Lloydbottom, *Your Money Counts* (Crown Financial Ministries, 2008)

- Stephen K de Silva, *Money and the Prosperous Soul: Tipping the scales of favour and blessing* (Chosen, 2010)

Session 5: Consuming Worship

 AIM: To see the distinction between the 'righteous' and the 'wicked' and to be challenged to commit ourselves afresh to God.

TO SET THE SCENE

Talk about commitment. What things have you committed to in your life and how was that commitment marked? Do you stick at things tenaciously, or make a commitment and then move on after a while?

Read the passage together:

"You have said harsh things against me," says the LORD.

"Yet you ask, 'What have we said against you?'

"You have said, 'It is futile to serve God. What did we gain by carrying out his requirements and going about like mourners before the LORD Almighty? But now we call the arrogant blessed. Certainly the evildoers prosper, and even those who challenge God escape.'"

Then those who feared the LORD talked with each other, and the LORD listened and heard. A scroll of remembrance was written in his presence concerning those who feared the LORD and honoured his name.

"They will be mine," says the LORD Almighty, "in the day when I make up my treasured possession. I will spare them, just as in compassion a man spares his son who serves him. And you will again see the distinction between the righteous and the wicked, between those who serve God and those who do not.

"Surely the day is coming; it will burn like a furnace. All the arrogant and every evildoer will be stubble, and that day that is coming will set them on fire," says the LORD Almighty. "Not a root or a branch will be left to them. But for you who revere my name, the sun of righteousness will rise with healing in its wings. And you will go out and leap like calves released from the stall. Then you will trample down the wicked; they will be ashes under the soles of your feet on the day when I do these things," says the LORD Almighty.

"Remember the law of my servant Moses, the decrees and laws I gave him at Horeb

for all Israel.

"See, I will send you the prophet Elijah before that great and dreadful day of the LORD comes. He will turn the hearts of the fathers to their children, and the hearts of the children to their fathers; or else I will come and strike the land with a curse."

Malachi 3:13-4:6

The last of the accusations and questions kicks off our passage today. The Israelite people seem genuinely surprised that God accuses them of saying harsh things. It indicates that outwardly the people may not have been saying anything negative, but their actions gave them away and, as we would say, spoke louder than their words. It is good to consider our actions and ask ourselves what they speak about our faith and our worship, both to God and to others who see us.

As our Bible study on Malachi comes to an end, let's remember that these prophet's words stand at the end of the Old Testament era. There is now a gap of 400 years while we turn the pages in our Bibles and start reading about the genealogy of Jesus: the day of the Lord is about to be fulfilled.

DISCUSS TOGETHER

1. Verse 14 contains three 'harsh things' that the Israelites have said to God:

- There is no use in ('it is futile to') serving God

- There is no profit ('gain') in carrying out his requirements, and

- There is no profit ('gain') in fasting and repentance.[3]

Put these into your own words and think through in what ways people say these things to God today.

 2. The Israelites' sentiments would seem to fit well in our consumer culture that expects everything to meet our individual needs and serve our personal interests.

Where do you see consumerism at work in your church? How could you counteract those tendencies?

> **My thoughts and notes....**
>
> *futile*
> *Empty meaning*
> *it isn't*

---

3   W. Kaiser, *Malachi*, 98.

How does this apply to me? **3.** Have you ever had times when you've looked at your life and at how you have served God and just thought, 'this isn't fair, I deserve more from God'?

What has helped you in those times?

4. It is encouraging to see that, despite Malachi's words, a remnant of faithful people remains within Israel. What are the differences between what we see in verses 14-15 and verses 16-18?

5. Out of the spiritual and cultural crisis described by Malachi, a group of faithful Israelites respond by getting together and discussing the situation. By way of response, they make their commitment to God and to each other by writing a scroll of remembrance about themselves.

Put yourself in their situation: how do you think they might have felt? What do you think they said when they met together? What do you think they actually did?

Can you think of a moment when, in the face of what is going on around you, you have had to make a public act to signal your intention of living differently? Maybe you are in a situation like that today?

What does the Bible say? **6.** The idea that God's people are his sons, or his children, is a very strong theme that runs throughout the whole Bible. Using the Bible verses given in the Leader's Notes (and of course any other verses that people may know), have a look at this topic and see what can you find out about the theme of sonship and adoption?

What does it mean to you to be God's child, rather than simply his subject?

7. The description of the 'day of the Lord' in chapter 4 holds in fine balance the notions of judgement and salvation. Discuss together your thoughts on this:

What is shocking about the language of verse 3?

Do you think we get the balance between judgement and salvation right in our churches and/or in our own lives?

8. Finish your discussion time together by looking back over these five sessions. What are the things you remember? What have you enjoyed about looking at Malachi? What have you not enjoyed? What have you learnt? Has anything changed in you as a result of these sessions?

WORSHIP

Re-read Malachi 4:2 and take some time to reflect on that beautiful imagery. Sit quietly and ask someone to read that verse out, slowly and prayerfully, maybe saying it two or three times. Then sit in silence for five minutes or so and let the words sink into you. Have a time during which people can share anything they would like to concerning that verse and then pray together, thanking God for his promises.

DURING THE WEEK

The promise of God's salvation is so amazing that surely we want everyone to know about it! How often do we get opportunities to talk about our faith with other people? If we do not get enough opportunities it may just be that we are not asking God to open them up for us, so ask God to do that this week and be prepared and willing to tell other people about Jesus' salvation (remembering to use words that they will understand and not our familiar church jargon!).

FOR FURTHER STUDY

Discussion around the idea of the 'day of the Lord' takes us into the area of eschatology, or a study of the 'last things'. Is this something that you are familiar with? If you would like to get a better understanding of this subject then two very helpful books to read are:

- Russ Rook and Stephen Holmes (eds.), *What are We Waiting For: Christian hope and contemporary culture* (Paternoster, 2008)

- Tom Wright, *Surprised by Hope* (SPCK, 2007)

Leaders' Guide

TO HELP YOU LEAD

You may have led a group many times before or this may be your first time. Here is some advice on how to lead these studies.

▶ As a group leader, you don't have to be an expert or a lecturer. You are there to facilitate the learning of the group members – helping them to discover for themselves the wisdom in God's word. You should not be doing most of the talking or dishing out the answers, whatever the group expects from you!

▶ You do need to be aware of the group's dynamics, however. People can be quite quick to label themselves and each other in a group situation. One person might be seen as the expect, another the moaner who always has something to complain about. One person may be labelled as quiet and not expected to contribute; another person may always jump in with something to say. Be aware of the different type of individuals in the group, but don't allow the labels to stick. You may need to encourage those who find it hard to get a word in, and quieten down those who always have something to say. Talk to members between sessions to find out how they feel about the group.

▶ The sessions are planned to try and engage every member in active learning. Of course you cannot force anyone to take part if they don't want to, but it won't be too easy to be a spectator. Activities that ask everyone to write down a word, or talk in twos, and then report back to the group are there for a reason. They give everyone space to think and form their opinion, even if not everyone voices it out loud.

▶ Do adapt the sessions for your group as you feel is appropriate. Some groups may know each other very well and will be prepared to talk at a deep level. New groups may take a bit of time to get to know each other before making themselves vulnerable, but encourage members to share their lives with each other.

▶ You probably won't be able to tackle all the questions in each session so decide in advance which ones are most appropriate to your group and situation.

► Encourage a number of replies to each question. The study is not about finding a single right answer, but about sharing experiences and thoughts in order to find out how to apply the Bible to people's lives. When brainstorming, don't be too quick to evaluate the contributions. Write everything down and then have a look to see which suggestions are worth keeping.

► Similarly, encourage everyone to ask questions, voice doubts and discuss difficulties. Some parts of the Bible are difficult to understand. Sometimes the Christian faith throws up paradoxes. Painful things happen to us that make it difficult to see what God is doing. A group should be a safe place to express all of this. If discussion doesn't resolve the issue, send everyone away to pray about it between sessions, and ask your minister for advice.

► Give yourself time in the week to read through the Bible passage and the questions. Read the Leaders' notes for the session, as different ways of presenting the questions are sometimes suggested. However during the session don't be too quick to come in with the answer – sometimes people need space to think.

► Delegate as much as you like! The easiest activities to delegate are reading the text, and the worship sessions, but there are other ways to involve the group members. Giving people responsibility can help them own the session much more.

► Pray for group members by name, that God would meet with them during the week. Pray for the group session, for a constructive and helpful time. Ask the Lord to equip you as you lead the group.

THE STRUCTURE OF EACH SESSION

Feedback: find out what people remember from the previous session, or if they have been able to act during the week on what was discussed last time.

To set the scene: an activity or question to get everyone thinking about the subject to be studied.

Bible reading: it's important actually to read the passage you are studying during the session. Ask someone to prepare this in advance or go around the group reading a verse or two each. Don't assume everyone will be happy to read out loud.

Questions and activities: adapt these as appropriate to your group. Some groups may enjoy a more activity-based approach; some may prefer just to discuss the questions. Try out some new things!

Worship: suggestions for creative worship and prayer are included, which give everyone an opportunity to respond to God, largely individually. Use these alongside singing or other group expressions of worship. Add a prayer time with opportunities to pray for group members and their families and friends.

For next week: this gives a specific task to do during the week, helping people to continue to think about or apply what they have learned.

Further study: suggestions are given for those people who want to study the themes further. These could be included in the group if you feel it's appropriate and if there is time.

WHAT YOU NEED

A list of materials that are needed is printed at the start of each session in the Leaders' Guide. In addition you will probably need:

Bibles: the main Bible passage is printed in the book so that all the members can work from the same version. It is useful to have other Bibles available, or to ask everyone to bring their own, so that other passages can be referred to.

Paper and pens: for people who need more space than is in the book!

Flip chart: it is helpful to write down people's comments during a brainstorming session, so that none of the suggestions is lost. There may not be space for a proper flip chart in the average lounge, and having one may make it feel too much like a business meeting or lecture. Try getting someone to write on a big sheet of paper on the floor or coffee table, and then stick this up on the wall with blu-tack.

GROUND RULES

How do people know what is expected of them in a group situation? Is it ever discussed, or do we just pick up clues from each other? You may find it helpful to discuss some ground rules for the group at the start of this course, even if your group has been going a long time. This also gives you an opportunity to talk about how you, as the leader, see the group. Ask everyone to think about what they want to get out of the course. How do they want the group to work? What values do they want to be part of the group's experience; honesty, respect, confidentiality? How do they want their contributions to be treated? You could ask everyone to write down three ground rules on slips of paper and put them in a bowl. Pass the bowl around the group. Each person takes out a rule and reads it, and someone collates the list. Discuss the ground rules that have been suggested and come up with a top five. This method enables everyone to contribute fairly anonymously. Alternatively, if your group are all quite vocal, have a straight discussion about it!

NB Not all questions in each session are covered, some are self-explanatory.

ICONS

 The aim of the session

 Investigate what else the Bible says

 How does this apply to me?

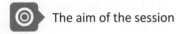 What about my church?

Session 1: Notes

FOR THIS FIRST SESSION ONLY

If at all possible, ask your group to take the time to read through the whole of Malachi in one sitting, before your first meeting together. It is helpful to read the whole thing as one block and to see how it all fits together, rather than only concentrating on the individual passages. There are only four chapters so it does not take long!

YOU WILL NEED

A number of blank sheets of A4 paper (probably around twelve, see below); pens, Bible concordances.

TO SET THE SCENE

The aim of this is to help everyone have a good foundational understanding of the history of Israel in the Old Testament. Your group may well have people in it with varying degrees of biblical knowledge, but it is surprising how even people who have been reading the Bible for many years do not always know the chronology of events in the Old Testament. Doing this exercise together helps build up that knowledge but not in a way embarrasses those whose understanding is limited. If there are a number in your group who you feel have only just 'got it' properly for the first time, you could always repeat the exercise in another session, maybe putting people into pairs and timing them as a competition.

For the major events, you can include the following: Creation, Fall, Noah/the Flood, Abra(ha)m, Joseph, the Exodus, Saul, David, Solomon, the Divided Kingdom, the Exile, and the Return from Exile. That makes twelve sheets of paper. Of course you can include more if you like.

DISCUSS TOGETHER

1. As highlighted above, it would be helpful if people can have read the whole of Malachi before you start this workbook as a group. Although we are breaking it down into five sessions, of course it was originally intended to be heard as one message. If most people have not been able to read it, you might like to start by reading it all through, so that people have some idea as to the scope of the prophecy.

Do give people the space to express their thoughts about the book. It does not make for the most pleasant of readings and it is helpful to let people say what they think, if need be, rather than try to pretend otherwise.

2. With this question, make sure people are aware that Israel's somewhat insolent questions form the structure around which this book works. You can point them to the other main questions in 1:6, 2:4, 2:17, 3:7 and 3:13.

3. 'I have loved you' is the key phrase for the whole of Malachi's prophecy and is the statement around which everything else is built.

4. With this question we reach the key Old Testament theme of God's choosing of one family to be the carriers of his special blessing. Jacob and Esau become the founders of the nations of Israel and Edom respectively (Genesis 32:28 and 25:30) and were rivals throughout the history of the Old Testament. This rivalry was begun by the Edomites when they refused to let Moses and the people walk through their territory (see Numbers 20), and relations between them never recovered. It is important to help people see that 'hate', in this context, does not mean what we understand it to mean, but is about ranking, or preference. Israel was the one chosen by God, but that did not mean that others had no place, or that it did not matter how they lived. Israel is in fact explicitly forbidden from 'abhoring' Edomites (Deuteronomy 23:7). Edom, however, following in the footsteps of Esau, seemed destined to be trouble makers and thus to bring trouble finally on themselves.

5 & 6. It might be interesting to reflect here on the sorts of times that people talk about in response to these two questions. It is important that we do not go down a simplistic road of, 'all went well for me then, so God must love me', or, 'things were bad then, so God doesn't love me'. We cannot only measure God's love for us in terms of whether things do or do not go well for us. How do we maintain faith in God's love regardless of the circumstances around us?

Do give people space here to share their stories.

Session 2: Notes

YOU WILL NEED

Bible concordances. A sheet of paper.

TO SET THE SCENE

The idea behind this exercise is simply to get people talking about something that shouldn't be a threatening subject, so that everyone has had a chance to say something and hear their own voice, and to introduce the idea of 'giving', which is one of the focuses of this passage in Malachi.

DISCUSS TOGETHER

1. It often seems to be a contradiction to talk about fearing a God who is our loving Father. That paradox can be seen in Exodus 20:20 which, in some translations, reads, 'Do not fear. God has come to test you, so that the fear of God will be with you to keep you from sinning'. What is helpful to understand is that a positive fear of God is about an attitude of trust and honour.

2. You could think of this in terms of people's work settings: imagine turning up on a Monday morning and saying, 'Well, boss, I can give you a couple of hours at the end of the day, but before that I've got more important things to do'! Or you could think of this in terms of the Taxman: imagine writing to the Inland Revenue and saying, 'I don't want to give you any money this year, but you could have this old car instead'!

3. This is a beautiful story that should be an encouragement to everyone who has wrestled with the problem of how to be generous with our money before God when it is a struggle to make ends meet. It shows that God looks at the heart of the giver, more than he looks at the gift. Perhaps it also shows that what God looks at is not only how much is given, but how much is left after the giving?

5. This is a tricky question and there is no right or wrong answer. On the one hand, it is counter-productive to be part of a church that has a style of worship that puts you off every week. On the other hand, we must beware our consumer 'because I'm worth it' culture that teaches us to expect everything to revolve around our desires and that places an emphasis on style rather than on content.

6. In our busy times, it can feel quite a sacrifice to give up a whole chunk of every Sunday to meet with your church. There are so many things that need to be done and, for those who work all week, the weekends can feel very pressured and precious. Give people the freedom to express any of this as they need to and be understanding rather than condemnatory. Look for ways to encourage people in your group in the midst of any busyness they may be feeling.

8. Make sure this question does not just lead into an opportunity to criticise your church and its worship leaders, who no doubt work hard and give their all to the task! Try to keep the discussion as positive as possible, helping people see how we can move from criticism to an active response.

Session 3: Notes

YOU WILL NEED

A large piece of paper and thick pen.

TO SET THE SCENE

In this session we will be covering a number of different topics. One of them is leadership as this passage is first addressed to Israel's priests. Leadership is something that we all experience, both through the leadership of others and through particular roles and positions that we ourselves occupy in life. The point of this exercise is to get people talking and thinking about leadership and, in particular, to see that leadership is not only about the person who runs your church.

DISCUSS TOGETHER

1. The reason for doing the two things, rather than just coming up with a list of biblical words for God, is that it can be easy to trot out the well-known descriptions (Creator, Almighty, Father etc) without actually taking time to think about what these things mean. So encourage people to think about what they are saying and work together at coming to a rich understanding of what is meant by the phrase, 'my name'.

Make sure you write these words down on a piece of paper because you will use them again in the Worship section.

2. There is an irony here as the pronouncement of blessings and curses was given to the people by Moses in the presence of the Levitical priests (Deuteronomy 27:9), and now here in Malachi these words are being directed back to the priests of Israel who should have known better. And they are being directed extremely strongly: the word for 'send' can also be translated 'hurl': 'I will hurl a curse upon you…'. This verse is almost a direct translation of Deuteronomy 28:20.

When you have looked at Deuteronomy 28, give space for any comments or thoughts that people might have.

3. Use this question to bring together the previous two questions and to stimulate people to think through how these words might be relevant today.

4. The relationship between the priests and the Levites in the Old Testament is a very confusing one. The Levites were the descendants of Levi, one of the sons of Jacob/Israel, and they became the Levitical tribe. Aaron was the first-born son of a Levite (Exodus 2:1, 6:20) and became Moses' right-hand man. It was the descendants of Aaron who were chosen to be the priests of Israel (Leviticus 8:1-4). The rest of the tribe of Levi were set apart to assist the priests in their work. Thus the whole of the Levitical tribe could be described as priests and priestly, although strictly speaking it was only those who were descendants of Aaron who were allowed to be priests. In our passage, Malachi uses Levi to represent the whole priestly class.

5. Just make sure that this question does not turn into an excuse to criticise your church leaders!

6. It is so important that we do not only think of leadership only from an internal church perspective, and there may be people in your group who would appreciate regular prayer and support for the positions that they hold throughout the week. Remember too that this does not only happen in the workplace: a parent is a leader when at home looking after their children.

7. In the first part of this question you might, for example, think of Jesus' prayer for unity in John 17; 1 Corinthians 12 and the picture of the church being the body of Christ; or Paul's words in Romans 4 about God being the father of all who believe, but this is not an exhaustive list.

9. It hardly need be said that this is a potentially emotive topic as you may have people in your group who have been through divorce themselves or others who may be struggling in their marriage and currently considering divorce, either openly or in secret. Remember not to assume you know what is going on in people's lives and to give people an opportunity to say what they want. You may want to have thought this question through beforehand and have it in your mind where you want the discussion to go.

It might also be helpful to know, in case any discussion hinges around this verse, that verse 15 is notoriously difficult to translate and we should beware of resting too heavy an argument on the translation given in our Bibles.

Session 4: Notes

YOU WILL NEED

Just yourselves and your Bibles.

TO SET THE SCENE

Part of what we are looking at in this session is money, giving and personal generosity and this question is a fun way to get us thinking about that whole area.

DISCUSS TOGETHER

1. Theodicy is the big issue that our passage kicks off with - or, in other words, the problem of evil. It is something that we all have to wrestle with: is it possible to acknowledge the reality of evil and at the same time believe in a God who is both loving and all-powerful? Many books have been written on the subject and there are no easy answers. However, it can be a positive thing for people simply to be given the space to talk about difficult topics such as this, rather than feeling that Christianity is about having all the answers sewn up. So allow people to talk about their own thoughts and feelings here.

2. By telling the people that he will send his messenger, God is refuting the Israelites' claims that he is absent and inactive.

3. Malachi was the last prophet to speak in the Old Testament period. Earlier prophets both foretold the destruction of Jerusalem and the exile, and looked forward to the time when the people would return from exile and Israel would be re-established as a nation, with Yahweh at the centre. However, by Malachi's time it was clear that post-exilic Israel was far from what had been expected. As immediate hopes diminished, so there arose a strand of the prophetic that began looking forward to a time when Yahweh would send his chosen one to bring about the full restoration of Israel in the way that the prophets had spoken of. This can be seen in the Servant Songs of Isaiah (eg. Isaiah 52:13 – 53:12). Right from the beginning, Christians have seen these expectations as being fulfilled in the person of Jesus.

Traditionally the focus of Jesus' incarnation has been on his dealing with personal sin, yet here the emphasis is on how his coming is an answer to the question, 'Where is the God of justice?'. Explore together how the two are linked.

5. The Old Testament prophets are unanimous in declaring that neglecting to look after people's needs is unacceptable for God's people. In our world today, in which injustice is rife, we help people best by not only taking care of their immediate needs but by also tackling the root causes of poverty. To do that we should play our part both by working within the system to see it changed, and by speaking into it through campaigning.

7. The Israelites were expected to tithe a tenth of their produce (see Leviticus 27: 30-33) but there is nothing in the New Testament to suggest that that this practice should continue today. The main instruction, instead, is that our giving should be a priority, regular, and as much as we can afford (1 Corinthians 16:1-2). However, some take the view that the principle of 10% is at least a helpful standard to keep to.

8. It is too personal to ask a direct question on how generous people are with their money. Instead, looking at the example of others can often inspire us to change and be more giving.

9. Money and giving are tricky topics that can leave us feeling defensive, guilty, confused or just downright depressed! However, it need not lead to any of those feelings and, if handled properly, can instead lead to us being used by God to bless others in a wonderful way. It is a subject that we are rarely happy to talk about, except in a general way. Is there a way that, as a group, you can help each other be more open about your money?

Session 5: Notes

YOU WILL NEED

Just yourselves and your Bibles.

TO SET THE SCENE

In the middle of today's passage we get our only glimpse of the few people who have remained faithful to Yahweh despite the general apathy and shallowness of the majority of the nation. These people have maintained their commitment to God and keep that going by writing in the scroll of remembrance. It takes commitment for us, too, to keep walking with God today.

DISCUSS TOGETHER

1. The Hebrew for 'use', that the NIV translates as 'futile' carries the meaning of being empty: in other words, the Israelites are saying that it is meaningless to serve God.

2. Consumerism is an extremely strong force in our society today and we bring its values into all areas of our lives, including our relationships and our faith. We increasingly now expect our church and our relationship with Jesus to serve us rather than the other way round. If they do not then we move on to somewhere or something else. Long-term commitment is a low priority.

3. These can be very real feelings, particularly for people who have made significant life choices that they felt called to do by God. Do not try to provide answers for anyone who carries these feelings, but let them voice their thoughts and find their own solutions.

4. The two key differences are, firstly, what attitude the people have towards God, and correspondingly, how God then responds to them. You might like to point people to Isaiah 58 which shows a similar thing: the people wonder why God seems silent and distant, but the reason is that they are putting on an outward show only and not worshipping God through living just lives.

5. The 'scroll of remembrance' is probably not akin to the more ethereal 'book of life' of Revelation 20 or Psalm 69, but was a literal scroll, maybe something like King Xerxes' book of chronicles in Esther 6:1.

6. Some helpful verses you can look at are Exodus 4:22, Isaiah 1:2, Jeremiah 3:9, Hosea 11:1, John 1:12-13, Romans 8:15-25, Galatians 3:26-4:7.

7. Historically the Church has swung from one extreme to the other, either emphasising judgement to the detriment of God's love and his salvation, or emphasising salvation to the detriment of God's wrath and his judgement.

Acts – Building A People Of Faith

Based on the timeless book of Acts, this will help you uncover the truth of God's word and apply it to your own life.
SHB1327B

Daniel – Faith Under Fire

Daniel's faith was literally tested by fire, but his God – and our God – proves himself faithful in the most extreme of situations.
SHB1351B

David – After God's Heart

This workbook explores David's overwhelming desire for intimacy with God, and shows how we can also be those 'after God's own heart'.
SHB1324B

Exodus – Mission Of God

This workbook shows how mission is God's big idea, and challenges Christians to get involved in what God is doing.
SHB1356B

Grace – God's Amazing Gift

Looking at grace through the life of Gideon and parts of the New Testament, this workbook will help you uncover the truth of God's grace and apply it to your own life.
SHB1314B

John – Jesus At The Centre

Discover more about Jesus by looking at some of the key passages from John's gospel – inspire yourself and others to put faith into action.
SHB1329B

Matthew – Sermon On The Mount

Covering the whole of Matthew 5-7, this workbook provides the perfect introduction to the Sermon On The Mount and its radical challenges.
SHB1317B

Passion – Finding An Unshakeable Hope

Exploring the significance of the cross and resurrection for our lives, hopes and relationships will help us grow in confidence and in the character and grace of God.
SHB1319B

Psalms – Cries From The Heart

A study on 8 Psalms designed to help your small group express their heart to God while seeking God's heart for them.
SHB1315B

Ruth – Love, Honour And Obey

Ruth put her mother-in-law's needs before her own and God honoured her decision in ways she could never have imagined.
SHB1320B

Worship – One True King

The life of Daniel shows us that worship is about offering our whole lives to God.
SHB1326B

Yahweh – God In All His Fullness

7 studies which seek to guide you into a deeper grasp of the magnificence of God.
SHB1389B